THE SMITHSONIAN

GARDENER'S JOURNAL

GALISON BOOKS
GMG Publishing, New York

A Galison Book
Published by GMG Publishing Corp.
25 West 43rd Street
New York, NY 10036

ISBN 0-939456-43-5

Designer: Marilyn Rose
Managing Editor: Hillary Huber
Publisher: Gerald Galison
Coordinated by: Susan Bates;
Smithsonian Institution

With special thanks to
the Smithsonian Institution
for permission to use
these illustrations and
to the following good people:

James R. Buckler
Spencer Crew
Susan Gurney
Marilyn Hanlon
Kathryn Meehan
Daisy Reese
Sally Tomlinson

Printed in Japan

INTRODUCTION

The *Smithsonian Gardener's Journal* has been developed for you to record the many fascinating happenings in your garden each year. It has been purposely created for the home gardener and gives month by month hints on landscape maintenance; flower, vegetable, and fruit gardening; as well as the treatment of indoor plants and decorations.

Gardeners throughout history have kept journals similar to this one. Many of our founding fathers, including George Washington and Thomas Jefferson, shared a love of gardens and gardening and kept extensive journals on the successes and failures in their gardens. They made careful observations on meteorological information concerning temperature, moisture, early frosts, or extended cloud covers during the year—all conditions that would have affected the quality of their gardens. They would often include comments on a specific variety of plant or gardening technique that they had admired in their travels.

I have always found it fascinating to peruse the old seed and nursery catalogs that we have acquired for the Office of Horticulture over the past 15 years. It was through the foresight of Mr. W. Atlee Burpee, who founded the W. Atlee Burpee Company in 1876, to keep accurate records that we better understand the horticultural industry of the late 19th century.

Mr. Burpee saved not only all of his company's catalogs but also those of his competitors, and made comparative notations in them about seed quality, price, and availability. These records have become an invaluable research tool for us today.

The gardening hints in the margins of this journal are to tantalize you into starting work on your garden early in the year. All too often we forget that we must plant the seeds in our garden months in advance, or order specific plants before they disappear from the marketplace. Each year, hundreds of new varieties of plants are introduced to the horticultural world. Man has always been fascinated by the hybridizing of new varieties, developing unusual and exciting colors, improving resistance to insects and diseases, and increasing the plant's ability to tolerate drastic changes in temperature, humidity, or light. It is fun to experiment with different varieties and, of course, you would want to note the results in your journal.

We recommend that you begin recording all pertinent details about your garden each year as part of your "New Year's Resolutions"—but you must continue to make your notes regularly if you intend to refer to the journal from year to year. Here at the Smithsonian, all of our plants are treated as collection items. In order to record their history, we have established a simple

accessioning and records system utilizing the last two digits of the year followed by a numerical sequence of each plant variety acquired during that year. You could follow a similar system by utilizing this journal to record each plant acquired, its parentage, its source, and any other pertinent data. It is also extremely helpful to photograph your garden during the year and keep the results in your journal for easy reference. As part of our record-keeping, we photograph our grounds seasonally, particularly individual flower beds, hanging baskets, and urn plantings. This records color combinations and which plants look best together. It is easy to forget these details unless they are recorded. In addition to your accession records and photographs, a simple labeling system (e.g., embossed aluminum tags) would help you keep up with the plants in your garden.

During the winter months, before planting time, peruse all of the marvelous seed catalogs available to map out a planting strategy for your garden. This is also a good time to inventory your existing garden in detail and develop a plot plan to scale on graph paper. After you have surveyed the existing conditions in your garden (such as soil analysis, drainage, sun and wind orientation, circulation, good and/or bad views, utilities, permanent plantings and structures, and microclimates), you could then begin to plan your garden.

A well-planned garden typically can be divided into three basic areas: public, service, and private. In the public area, such as your front lawn, keep the plantings simple. Organize your service area so that your garden hoses, bicycles, parking, trash, and equipment are not only accessible but aesthetically pleasing. In your private garden area, indulge in creating terraces and patios for relaxing; organize vegetable, flower, and fruit gardens; and set aside specific areas for children to play.

By following the procedure outlined above, you will end up with a master plan. Each area or project could be given a priority number, which would allow you to plan your garden development over the upcoming years and relieve you of the pressures of trying to accomplish too much in your garden at one time. Your garden should be a pleasurable place; therefore, I suggest that you make notes in your journal each year of ideas for labor-saving techniques—such as mulching, edging, and staking—and the type of equipment that would make your garden more enjoyable to work in the following year.

If possible, incorporate a small greenhouse, cold frame, or an indoor light garden to extend your gardening season. In my own garden, I thoroughly enjoy using exotic and unusual tropical standards, topiaries, and large plants in tubs; however, winter temperatures prohibit me from leaving these plants outside. In order to protect them, I simply modified an old porch by covering the screens with a double layer of clear polyethylene and put insulation under the floor joists, thus creating an inexpensive winter gallery. Those plants requiring higher light conditions are placed under fluorescent lights. It's marvelous to see blooming plants during the winter months.

As your gardening year evolves, if you record your thoughts regularly in your journal about your successes and failures, changes you would like to make, the color combinations you liked, and even the plants you admired in other gardens, then this journal will always be an invaluable tool in creating the next year's garden.

The illustrations throughout this journal are from two very important Smithsonian Institution collections: the Office of Horticulture collection of nursery and seed catalogs (including the Burpee Collection), which date from the mid-19th century through today; and the Warshaw Collection of Business Americana in the National Museum of American History, which has a collection of business ephemera on the seed business, advertisements, and catalogs. Both of these collections are available for serious researchers and scholars to study.

We do hope you will enjoy your *Gardener's Journal* over the years and wish you great success with your garden. If you keep up the record of your garden, it will someday become a marvelous gift for your children and for future generations. Happy gardening!

James R. Buckler,
Director
Office of Horticulture
Smithsonian Institution

WELCOME

The Smithsonian Institution's Office of Horticulture was established in 1972 to create a full range of research and educational programs in horticulture for all of the Smithsonian's 15 museums and galleries. In addition, this office was asked to develop plans for the relandscaping of all of the Smithsonian Institution museum grounds (more than 32 acres) to become botanical and horticultural showplaces by the time the United States of America's Bicentennial would be celebrated in 1976.

Today, more than 45 professional gardeners, horticulturists, and grower-specialists carry out the original goals set in 1972. Each year, the office installs more than 100,000 seasonal annuals and perennials around the museum grounds. A range of 11 greenhouses contains a major collection of more than 35,000 rare and endangered species and hybrids including orchids, bromeliads, ivies, ferns, and others. Additional extensive collections include: 19th-century garden furniture, florists' accessories, and memorabilia; a horticultural library of more than 2,500 volumes on practical and historic horticulture; the Burpee Collection of more than 15,000 seed and nursery catalogs of the 19th and 20th century; and the Trees of Christmas Collection of more than 11,000 ornaments of cultural, ethnic, and historical importance. The new Enid A. Haupt Garden contains such features as the Granite and Islamic Gardens, an outstanding representation of 19th-century settees and urns, as well as an elaborate Victorian embroidery parterre.

We invite you to come and visit the Smithsonian Institution, which is open every day of the year except Christmas. We are very proud of our changing seasonal displays of plants, both on the grounds and throughout the interiors of the museums, and feel you will find them enjoyable. They may also provide you with ideas to take home to help you fulfill your own gardening goals.

NEW SEEDS

FROM
D.M. FERRY & CO.
Detroit, Mich.

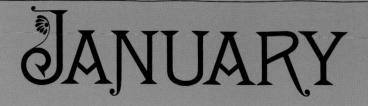

JANUARY

Peruse seed and nursery catalogs for new varieties. Check inventory records of stored bulbs, tubers, and seeds. Consult last year's diary for superior *vs.* inferior plants in your garden. Beginning January 1, keep an accurate notebook, recording both successes and failures in the garden.

Display

Bring in first of the forcing bulbs from the cold frame (or refrigerator, in the South). Place in semi-shaded spot—45 to 50°F —until sprouts are 2" to 3" tall; then move them to sunny window.

Take root cuttings of Oriental poppies, phlox, and gaillardias to provide spring plants. Roots should be cut into segments 2" long. Set in builder's sand and compost until well rooted.

Check fall-planted perennials and shrubs for frost heaving. If necessary, push root ball into soil with heel and firm new soil up, level with surrounding areas.

Order summer bulbs (*e.g.,* gladioli) and tubers (*e.g.,* begonias and dahlias) early to get named varieties.

Sow snapdragon, petunia, and ageratum seed in flats for summer garden. Because seeds are tiny, sow over ⅛" layer of milled sphagnum moss covering potting soil.

Vegetable Garden

Build cloches (glass or plastic covers) to cover areas tilled in fall. This will warm the soil and allow early February plantings.

Sow lettuce in cold frame; check plant varieties suited for your area.

Sow tomatoes, onions, and leeks in boxes; exclude light until seedlings germinate. Force rhubarb in dark cellar. (Use only its pinkish stems for making pies; rhubarb leaves are poisonous!)

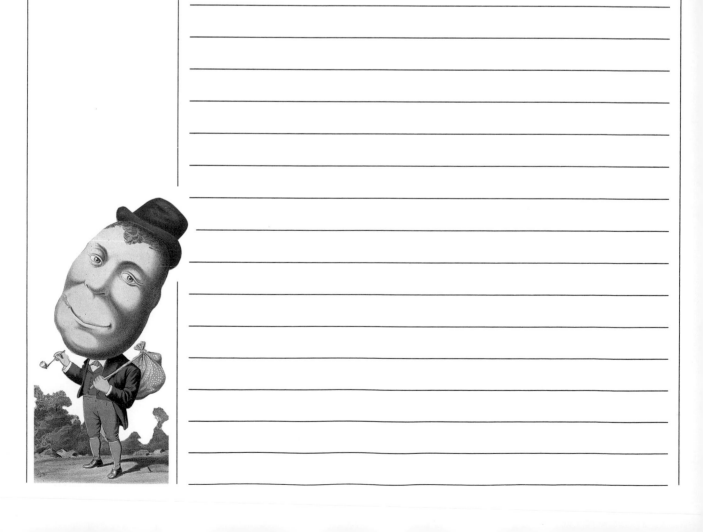

Indoor Garden

Check greenhouse or light garden for early-flowering cattleyas, and use for display.

Check all plants for disease and insect damage. Clean leaves of dust, remove dead leaves or broken branches, and spray with insecticide if necessary.

Use evergreen boughs left over from the holidays to protect cold frames or perennial beds.

FEBRUARY

To get best varieties, order *seeds* now for summer garden.

Work outside in good weather to clear branches and debris after winter storms.

Check if garden furniture needs repair or repainting. Send off mowers and tillers for maintenance. Clean and sharpen all tools.

Display

Check all perennial beds for heaving and mulch if needed.

Weather permitting, fork herbaceous border and add compost or well-rotted manure.

Prune varieties of *Buddleia davidii* to 12" above ground. Save branches to use as brushing in perennial beds or for garden peas.

Plant tuberous begonias, regale lily, and gloxinia tubers in flats of damp peat moss. Move them outdoors in June.

Prune trees and shrubs that flower in mid- to late summer.

ESTABLISHED 1852.

CALIFORNIA SEEDS

TREES AND NURSERY STOCK.

1888 Catalogue

W. R. STRONG & CO.

SACRAMENTO, CAL.

Vegetable Garden

Weather permitting, till green-manure crop sown in October and level with rake.

Weather permitting, sow turnips and early varieties of peas at end of month.

Sow radish; cover with straw or cloche.

Divide thyme and chives for herb garden.

For early succulent beets, sow in cold frames or under cloche.

Orchard

Fertilize apples, pears, and other spring fruit trees.

Remove any fruit from previous year to prevent disease and insect problems.

Prune fruit trees according to recommended practices.

THE $1600. TOMATO.

Indoor Garden

Sow lobelia, pansies, and violas in flats.

Pot young tomatoes from January sowing: Put singly into 3" to 4" pots; hold at 50°F temperature.

Sow cucumbers in 3" pot, excluding light until germination, and hold in sunny location until can be hardened off.

Force branches of early-spring flowering shrubs (*e.g.*, forsythia, spirea, azaleas) and trees (*e.g.*, magnolias, dogwood, redbud).

MARCH

Clean all beds of debris and old, dead plants.

Till soil for new beds.

Outdoor Garden

Dig and divide hardy perennials (*e.g.*, monarda, phlox, helenium, achillea, plumbago, etc.). Record dates of divisions and locations of plants.

Remove dead and diseased sections of roses.

Plant pansies, foxgloves, and forget-me-nots held in cold frames.

Check for early-flowering woodland plants; record locations in diary.

Prune and fertilize hedges.

Cut back all ornamental grasses; compost debris.

Vegetable Garden

Plant leeks, early lettuce, onion sets, peas, radishes, spinach, and turnips.

Transplant hardy vegetables such as cabbage, broccoli, cauliflower, celery, chives, onions. Cover with cloches if necessary.

Prepare new asparagus bed(s): Deep dig; add compost and/or manure.

Orchard

Uncover strawberries that were covered with straw in fall.

Plant young fruit trees.

Spray trees with dormant oil to control early insects; first check with the county extension agent for your area.

Fine prune espaliered fruit trees.

Indoor Garden

Begin repotting cattleya alliance group after flowering.

Repot all plants in new soil.

Sow annuals seed (*e.g.*, zinnia, nicotiana, and marigold) for summer garden.

Sow melon seed: Set ½" deep, in 3" pots; hold temperature at 65 to 70°F and keep soil moist.

Put plants sown in January and February into 3" pots; water. Heat from sun is increasing, so keep well watered if in greenhouse.

Bring spring-flowering Clivia into living area to show off these magnificent orange and yellow flowering bulbs.

APRIL

The busiest month in the garden! Keep sowing crops or you'll fall behind.

Finish tilling all beds to be planted before June.

Outdoor Garden

Finish planting herbaceous perennials. Lightly fork established borders between plants to loosen soil.

Do not mulch perennial borders yet.

Plant evergreen trees, shrubs, and hedges.

Prune early-flowering shrubs such as forsythia as soon as they have finished flowering. Remove old canes.

Tie clematis to support.

If daffodils have finished blooming, remove old flower heads and allow foliage to yellow.

Dig, divide, and replant daylilies, hostas, and ornamental grasses.

For best bloom, fall chrysanthemums and asters should be divided and replanted.

THE OLD RELIABLE SEEDSMAN

R.H. SHUMWAY.

R.H. SHUMWAY JR.

R.H. Shumway's

1900 ILLUSTRATED

GARDEN GUIDE

ROCKFORD · ILL.

Vegetable Garden

Add twigs or brushing for peas to climb.

Sow herbs in herb garden; divide mints, sorrel, and lovage for transplanting.

Continue sowing vegetables: Small sowings allow for a succession of harvest.

Plant potato tubers and seedlings of lettuce, broad beans, and leeks.

Plant new asparagus crowns in prepared beds and inspect old bed for early spears.

Plant strawberry plants as soon as received.

Orchard

Spray acording to schedule recommended by local county extension agent.

Graft trees early in month.

Tie espaliered fruits to frames if needed.

Lawn Care

Test soil for pH and follow recommendations for improvement.

Seed areas needing repair from winter damage.

Cut grass early. Use bag to catch clippings, or rake lawn to remove early thatch.

Indoor Garden

Pot January-sown tomatoes into final pot, or plant directly outside if weather permits.

Move all hardy bulbs forced during winter into cold frames; set them out in cutting garden in May.

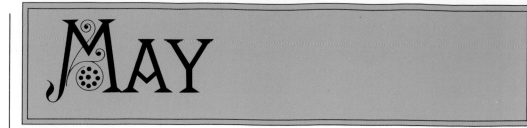

MAY

Early-planted salad crops can now be harvested.

Take time to enjoy the magnificent short-lived spring-flowering trees, shrubs, and vines.

Outdoor Garden

Cut grass long to encourage good root systems and to discourage weeds.

Remove dahlia tubers and large-leaf caladiums from root cellar; clean, divide, and plant in garden.

Place brushings or twigs in perennial beds for those plants that have a tendency to "flop."

Thin annuals planted in April; stake if necessary.

Plant out geraniums at end of month.

Start new compost heap.

Remove unsightly spring bulbs and reset in cut flower garden or in nursery area.

Set out petunias and/or marigolds in areas left vacant by removal of spring bulbs.

Vegetable Garden

Harvest asparagus, onions, radishes, turnips, spinach, and early strawberries.

Sow basil and dill in herb garden.

Plant herb plants in permanent garden spot.

Continue to sow beans, lettuce, radishes, squash, and carrots in small groups to prolong harvest.

Indoor Garden

Move all seedlings to cold frames to harden off; plant in garden as soil warms.

Move tuberous begonias to 6" pots.

Move rooted chrysanthemum cuttings into garden or into their final pots.

Groom all tropical plants to be moved outside in June.

Begin repotting and dividing cymbidium, phalaenopsis and paphiopedilum orchids.

JUNE

Fear of frost should be over in all areas of the country, so move all tender plants to garden.

Fertilize all trees, shrubs, ground covers, and other garden areas as needed.

DUNLAP'S SEEDS

NASHUA N.H.

GOOD HARVEST FROM GOOD SEED.

Outside Garden

Plant window boxes and tubs early in month and place in garden.

Remove dead flowers from lilacs, azaleas, and rhododendrons.

Divide German iris where crowded; discard weak fans.

Mulch annual and perennial borders to keep soil cool and retain moisture.

Water garden well if weather is dry.

Place hanging baskets outside in final location.

Continue to watch roses carefully for aphids or black spot. Remove all dead leaves, and spray as needed.

Sow ornamental cabbage and kale for fall accent plants in display garden.

Remove unwanted suckers from trees and shrubs.

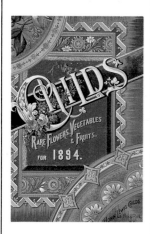

Vegetable Garden

Continue to sow late crops. Hoe between rows to keep down weeds.

Harvest early lettuce and radishes. Harvest cauliflower, broccoli, and brussels sprouts; blanch and freeze extras.

Thin vegetables as needed.

Remove flower heads from autumn-sown onions.

Indoor Garden

Move all indoor plants outside for summer. Choose location suitable for each plant.

Visit local botanical gardens, arboreta, and museums for new ideas and displays of the most up-to-date plants or information.

JULY

A rewarding month for those who made an early start!

Watch for insect and disease problems.

Don't trust to memory! Keep detailed records of successes and failures in this garden diary.

Outside Garden

Take softwood cuttings of azaleas, boxwood, and yews; propagate in sand.

Water garden deeply if weather is dry.

Feed and top-dress plants in boxes, tubs, and hanging baskets. Remove dead flowers and pinch back annuals (such as petunias) to encourage new flowers.

Stake tall ornamental grasses to prevent them from flopping over later in the summer.

Tag plants to be moved later if in wrong place or color combination is incorrect.

GOOD HARVEST FROM GOOD SEED.

Vegetable Garden

Harvest vegetables as ready, can or freeze excess, and place all debris on compost pile.

Begin gathering herbs for drying; save seeds in dry container for next year.

Sow last of summer lettuce.

Continue to stake tomatoes and remove all side shoots.

Peg down strawberry runners for next crop.

Harvest onions when foliage turns yellow and collapses; store in dry location or in mesh onion sacks.

Pick early apples for applesauce.

AUGUST

Visit horticultural shows and county fairs.

Make notes in garden journal for improving the general landscape, cut flower gardens, perennial and annual borders, orchard, and vegetable-herb garden.

Outside Garden

Take semi-hardwood cuttings of shrubs such as hydrangeas, azaleas. Cuttings should be kept moist in a shaded frame.

Keep all borders weeded and watered.

Pinch and tie chrysanthemums in garden early in month; feed and water well.

Prepare new lawn areas for seeding late in month and repair worn spots.

Cut and dry statice, strawflowers, cockscomb, teasel, and gomphrena for use in winter bouquets.

Try Rice's Seeds

Grown by the
Jerome B. Rice Seed Co.
CAMBRIDGE VALLEY SEED GARDENS
CAMBRIDGE, N.Y.

Vegetable Garden

Feed tomatoes for late harvest.

Harvest potatoes, onions, cucumbers, and melons as ready.

Cut fresh herb sprigs to use in jellies for holiday gifts: Start with white grape juice or apple juice as base, and add pectin to solidify.

Cut sprigs of tarragon, chives, thyme, and rosemary and make herbal vinegars. They'll bring a taste of summer to winter salads.

Harvest blackberries and raspberries when ready, and use extra for jellies and jams.

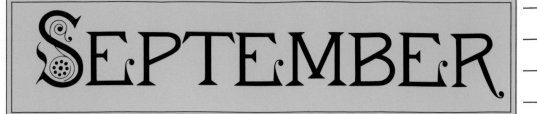

SEPTEMBER

Final month to survey summer garden plantings and make notes in diary.

Cut and dry Queen Anne's lace and goldenrod for fall bouquets and holiday decorations.

Look for special cones, pods, and dried grasses for arrangements.

Outdoor Garden

Cut and dry early grass plumes.

Take cuttings of evergreens such as privet, laurel, arborvitae, and late azaleas, and place in propagation area.

Divide and transplant Siberian iris.

Between now and November, plant peonies in full sun and rich soil.

Lift gladioli corms as foliage dies.

Plant lilies.

Later in month, clear garden of summer bedding plants. Fork over, level, and plant chrysanthemums, pansies, or ornamental cabbage and kale grown in pots.

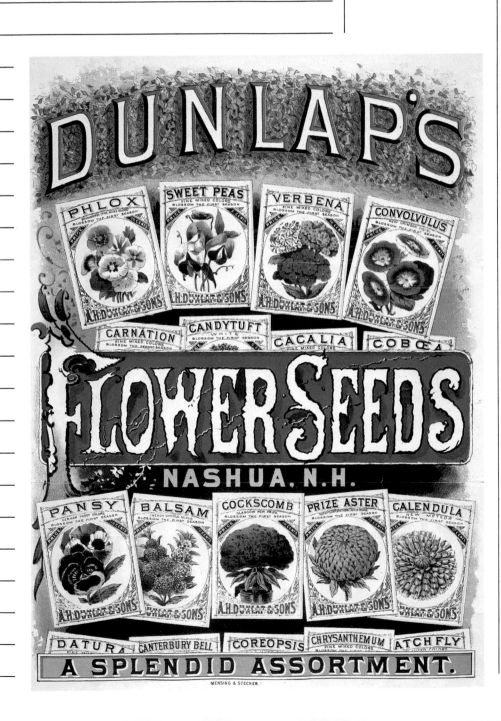

DWARF BLACK WAX BEAN.
THE EARLIEST IN CULTIVATION.
FOR SALE HERE.

Vegetable Garden

Lift potatoes and dry.

Take cuttings of herbs: sage, rosemary, thyme, rose geraniums, etc.

Sow seeds or cool crops such as lettuce, spinach, turnips.

Cut off large leaves of parsley to encourage new growth.

Cut last of summer herbs for drying.

Remove all debris from garden to compost pile.

Record data on success of all vegetables, and begin planning rotation of crops for next season.

Indoor Garden

Prepare all tropical and non-hardy plants for return indoors in early October.

Buy forcing bulbs such as paperwhite narcissus, amaryllis, and hyacinths; stagger potting.

OCTOBER

Don't be fooled by Indian summer: Watch out for early frosts.

Cut ornamental grass plumes before they begin to open to prevent shattering. Continue collecting cones and pods.

Label all plants that you may have neglected to label earlier.

Outside Garden

Plant English and Dutch iris.

Sod worn spots in lawns not seeded in early September.

Buy spring bulbs and plant early so roots have a chance to get well established. Add bone meal and water well after planting. Mark locations in display beds.

Apply slow-acting fertilizers, such as bone meal, where needed.

Clear future garden areas; till, and compost and manure. Leave garden area in rough condition to allow frost action.

Cut bittersweet for fall decoration.

Dig dahlias with forks, shake off soil, and dip tubers in fungicide solution. Let dry, and then store in cool area, such as root cellar, for winter.

BUIST'S EARLY MORNING STAR PEA.
The Earliest & most Productive Variety See Pages 94 & 95

BUIST'S
MAJESTIC TOMATO
THE LARGEST, FINEST FORMED
AND MOST SOLID VARIETY.

SEE PAGE 115.

_____

_____

_____

_____

_____

_____

_____

_____

_____

_____

_____

_____

_____

_____

_____

_____

_____

_____

_____

_____

_____

_____

_____

_____

_____

Vegetable Garden

Remove all leftover plants; move debris to compost pile.

Harvest pumpkins, Indian corn, and winter squash.

Till garden areas, and sow winter wheat or ryegrass for green-manure crop.

Early in the month, dig and pot all tender herbs to be brought indoors— *e.g.*, rosemary and rose geraniums.

Plant garlic cloves—3" deep and 5" apart—in sunny spot. They'll be up in early spring.

Indoor Garden

Early in month, groom all non-hardy plants to be returned to house; spray with insecticides as needed.

Leave cymbidium orchids outside until first light frost to encourage flower-bud initiation.

Continue planting paperwhite narcissus, hyacinths, and amaryllis for forcing.

Repot oncidium orchids.

November

Build cold frames for later use.

Enjoy the last of Indian summer.

Outdoor Garden

Cut back all perennials. Clean beds, and mulch tender plants.

Replant into ground all perennials that were used as tubbed material in summer.

Collect leaves for compost. (Beech and oak leaves are best.)

Store all garden furniture; tag those pieces to be repaired or repainted during dull winter months.

Clean all tools—oil to prevent rusting—and tag those pieces of equipment that will need servicing during winter.

Finish preparing beds with compost and manure for early spring plantings.

Vegetable Garden

Harvest fall turnips, lettuce, and spinach.

Cut fresh parsley.

Cover strawberries with salt hay to get fruit for Christmas.

Before ground freezes, dig hole for planting of live Christmas tree. Store soil to be packed around root ball in garage.

Plant roses; mulch.

After ground freezes, cover hardy chrysanthemums with straw mulch to protect against freezing and thawing.

Indoor Garden

Prune all interior plants, fertilize lightly, and inspect for insect and disease damage.

Check all plant varieties to see if they can tolerate temperature ranges in your home.

Make fall flower arrangements and begin dried holiday wreaths. Make fragrant pomander balls using apples or oranges: Push whole cloves in to fruit, dust with orrisroot, and hang with decorative ribbon.

Make potpourri mixtures from flowers, leaves, and stems collected in summer; add potpourri oils if necessary.

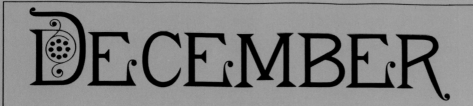

DECEMBER

Enjoy the fruits of your summer labors: Make a special trip to your root and /or canning cellar.

Sit back before a blazing fire and reflect on your gardening year. Make notes and prepare for seed catalogs to arrive in January.

Shop for horticultural books as gifts.

HENDERSON'S
NEW RED
SUNFLOWE
SE:
OPPOSITE 1

SEED ANNUAL.

1897

D. M. FERRY & CO.
DETROIT, MICH.

THE CALVERT LITH.CO.DETROIT.

Outdoors

Prune evergreen trees and shrubs for indoor and outdoor holiday decorations.

Protect prized evergreens (*e.g.*, boxwood) from potential snow and ice damage by placing snow fence or lathing over plant.

Add mulch to late perennials and evergreens.

Fill window boxes with winter-flowering pansies or wallflowers.

Indoors

Unless you were successful in forcing your own, purchase poinsettias early in December, for brilliant color throughout the house.

Test garden seed saved during the season: Place small amount on moist paper towel; if 50 to 60 percent germinate, then you can plant with confidence in spring.

Enjoy your forced bulbs for the holidays.

Make Christmas critters from pods and cones collected throughout the year. Use them to decorate your tree or as special touches for holiday packages.

Sprinkle dried herbs on fire to add fragrance to the room before guests arrive.

Set up a fluorescent-light garden to start seedlings and to grow specimen begonias, geraniums, and other tropical plants, as well as to propagate plants for next year's garden.

GLOSSARY

accession:	To assign a number to a plant, piece of garden furniture, or equipment when received and to record that number, the date, condition, and description of the object in a special notebook often called a register.
accession number:	Number assigned in consecutive order to a collection object by which the object can be identified. This number usually has letters to identify the collection and numerals to identify the year of receipt and rank in which it was received.
annual:	A plant living only one year or season.
aphid:	An insect that sucks sap from stems or leaves.
arboretum:	A collection of trees and shrubs grown for study and display.
black spot:	A fungus disease causing black spots on the leaves and stems of roses and other plants.
botanical garden:	A garden for the exhibition and scientific study of living plant collections.
bromeliads:	Members of the Bromelia family. Most are tropical American plants such as the genera *Ananas* (pineapple), *Tillandsia* (Spanish moss), and others; many are grown for their ornamental value.
brushing:	The use of twigs to stabilize perennials and small bush-type vegetables.
"Christmas critters":	Ornaments resembling animals, birds, and insects imaginatively created from natural materials.
circulation:	In landscape design, the system of walkways or driveways determining routes of pedestrian or vehicular traffic.
cold frame:	A bottomless, boxlike, usually glass-covered structure placed over a bed of earth to protect plants. Often constructed of window sash; the top should be adjustable for ventilation.
compost:	A mixture of various decaying organic materials, such as dead leaves, used for fertilizer.
corm:	A fleshy, bulblike base of a stem, as in crocus and gladiolus, found below ground, that stores reserve food.
cultivar:	A variety of plant that has been produced only under cultivation.
county extension agent:	A trained horticulturist who is available, in most jurisdictions, to answer questions posed by the public.

division:	A form of propagation by which the separation of plant roots or cutting in half of entire plant makes several plants.
dormant oil:	Applied to trees and shrubs to control diseases and pests. The oil can be better tolerated by plants in dormancy rather than in leaf.
espalier:	A trellis or framework on which a tree or shrub is trained to grow flat, often in a symmetrical pattern; also, the tree or shrub so trained.
exotic:	A plant introduced from another part of the world; not native to its current environment.
fans:	A group of iris leaves. An iris division must include a fan with its section of rhizome.
forcing (bulbs):	To cause to grow by artificially accelerating the normal processes—usually by raising the temperature.
fork (forking over):	Loosening soil by using a garden fork; shallow digging or working of prongs in soil with twisting motion.
fungicide:	A chemical that kills fungi or checks their growth. Copper salts and sulphur are among the most effective fungicides available.
germinate:	To begin to grow or sprout.
graft:	To unite a shoot or bud with a growing plant by insertion or placing in close contact.
green manure:	A quick-grown cover crop that is dug back into the ground to improve the soil.
harden off:	To gradually acclimatize a plant to a lower, more fluctuating temperature and humidity.
hardiness:	A plant's ability to survive its environment.
heaving:	The upward movement of ground due to frost that dislodges plant roots.
herbaceous:	Not woody above ground.
horticulture:	The science or art of growing and displaying flowers, fruits, vegetables, and ornamental plants.
hybrid:	A plant produced by cross-breeding dissimilar plant parents.
microclimate:	The climate of a specific space within an area that is different from the climate within the area as a whole.
mulch:	A protective covering placed around plants to prevent evaporation of moisture and freezing of roots, and to control weeds.
orris root:	The fragrant rootstock of the German iris; used in perfumed products.
parterre:	A formal garden with plants arranged and often sheared to form a pattern; historically intended to be viewed from above.
perennial:	A plant living for several seasons.

potpourri:	A fragrant mixture of dried petals, leaves, oils, and/or spices; when stirred, its scent perfumes the surrounding area.
propagation:	The multiplication of plants.
prune:	The deliberate cutting off or shortening of stems or roots to render a plant more appropriate for its purpose or location, to improve its survival, or to stimulate its growth.
salt hay:	Hay made from grasses that inhabit salt marshes; especially useful as winter covering for hardy herbaceous perennials and low evergreens, as well as strawberries; does not mat nor rot as quickly as ordinary hay or straw; its seeds will germinate only in wet saline soil.
sphagnum moss:	A dried moss used as plant packing and rooting material. When milled, it is an excellent medium in which to sow seed. Its antiseptic quality inhibits growth of damping-off disease.
standard:	A plant trained or grafted to have a single, erect, treelike stem.
sucker:	Shoots developing from underground root or stem.
top-dressing:	A material spread over soil surface; differs from mulch in that its primary purpose is to supply nutrients rather than suppress weeds or conserve moisture.
topiary:	Shrubs and small trees trained and sheared into formal shapes.

BIBLIOGRAPHY

The Office of Horticulture branch of the Smithsonian Institution Libraries has a collection of books, periodicals, trade catalogs, and ephemeral material on historical and practical horticulture, garden history, and landscape design. Two significant areas of the collection for historical research are 15,000 seed and nursery catalogs, concentrated in the years 1885 through 1920, and a specially purchased group of 158 nineteenth and early twentieth century titles on American landscape design. Listed below is a selection of books from the Library on various topics and including titles of an historical interest from the nineteenth and early twentieth centuries. The starred items are suggested for the small home library on gardening.

Practical Gardening Techniques: Also good for special projects

Brickell, Christopher. *Pruning*. N.Y.: Simon and Schuster, 1979.

Browse, Philip McMillan. *Plant Propagation*. N.Y.: Simon and Schuster, 1979.

Buist, Robert. *The American Flower Garden Directory: Containing Practical Directions for the Culture of Plants in the Flower Garden, Hot-House, Green-House, Rooms, or Parlour Windows, for Every Month in the Year*. 2nd edition. Philadelphia: Carey & Hart, 1839.

*Bush-Brown, James. *America's Garden Book*. Revised edition by the New York Botanical Garden. N.Y.: Scribner, 1980.

Crockett, James Underwood. *Crockett's Victory Garden*. Boston: Little, Brown, & Co., 1977.

Faust, Joan Lee. *The New York Times Garden Book*. 2nd edition. N.Y.: Knopf, 1973.

Henderson, Peter. *Practical Floriculture; a Guide to the Successful Cultivation of Florists' Plants, for the Amateur and Professional Florist*. N.Y.: Orange Judd and Company, 1869.

Jekyll, Gertrude. *Wood and Garden; Notes and Thoughts, Practical and Critical, of a Working Amateur*. London, N.Y.: Longmans, Green, and Co., 1899.

Johnson, Hugh. *The Principles of Gardening: A Guide to the Art, History, Science, and Practice of Gardening*. N.Y.: Simon and Schuster, 1979.

Long, Elias A. *Ornamental Gardening for Americans*. N.Y.: Orange Judd, 1885.

Swindells, Philip. *The Overlook Water Gardener's Handbook*. Woodstock, N.Y.: Overlook Press, 1984.

Thomas, Graham Stuart. *The Art of Planting, or, The Planter's Handbook*. London: J.M. Dent, 1984.

Tricker, William. *The Water Garden*. N.Y.: A.T. De La Mare Printing and Pub. Co., 1897.

Houseplants: For the parlor gardener

Elbert, George. *The Indoor Light Gardening Book*. N.Y.: Crown Publishers, 1973.

Gaines, Richard L. *Interior Plantscaping: Building Design for Interior Foliage Plants*. N.Y.: Architectural Record Books, 1977.

Herwig, Rob. *The Good Housekeeping Encyclopedia of House Plants*. N.Y.: Hearst Books, 1985.

Huxley, Anthony. *The World Guide to House Plants*. N.Y.: Scribner, 1983.

Kramer, Jack. *The Complete Book of Terrarium Gardening*. N.Y.: Scribner, 1974.

Manaker, George H. *Interior Plantscapes: Installation, Maintenance, and Management*. Englewood Cliffs, N.J.: Prentice-Hall, 1981.

*Powell, Charles C. *Ortho's Complete Guide to Successful Houseplants*. San Francisco: Chevron Chemical Co., 1984.

Randolph, Cornelia J. *The Parlor Gardener: A Treatise on the House Culture of Ornamental Plants*. Boston: J.E. Tilton & Co., 1861.

Williams, Henry T. *Window Gardening: Devoted Specially to the Culture of Flowers and Ornamental Plants for Indoor Use and Parlor Decoration*. 7th edition. N.Y.: H.T. Williams, 1874.

Annuals, Perennials, Bulbs: To create year-round interest in your garden

Brown, Emily. *Landscaping with Perennials.* Portland, Ore.: Timber Press, 1986.

Grounds, Roger. *Ornamental Grasses.* N.Y.: Van Nostrand Reinhold, 1981.

Hebb, Robert S. *Low Maintenance Perennials.* N.Y.: Quadrangle/The New York Times Book Co., 1975.

Hudak, Joseph. *Gardening with Perennials Month by Month.* N.Y.: Quadrangle/New York Times Book Co., 1976.

Martin, Laura C. *The Wildflower Meadow Book; a Gardener's Guide.* Charlotte, N.C.: East Woods Press, 1986.

Nehrling, Arno and Irene Nehrling. *The Picture Book of Annuals.* N.Y.: Hearthside Press, 1966.

Newcomb, Peggy Cornett. *Popular Annuals of Eastern North America 1865–1914.* Washington, D.C.: Dumbarton Oaks, 1985.

Phillips, Harry R. *Growing and Propagating Wild Flowers.* Chapel Hill, N.C.: University of North Carolina Press, 1985.

Rand, Edward Sprague. *Bulbs: A Treatise on Hardy and Tender Bulbs and Tubers.* Boston: J.E. Tilton and Co., 1866.

Rix, Martyn. *The Bulb Book; a Photographic Guide to over 800 Hardy Bulbs.* London: Pan Books Ltd., 1981.

* *Taylor's Guide to Annuals.* Boston: Houghton Mifflin Co., 1986.

* *Taylor's Guide to Bulbs.* Boston: Houghton Mifflin Co., 1986.

* *Taylor's Guide to Perennials.* Boston: Houghton Mifflin Co., 1986.

Wyman, Donald. *Ground Cover Plants.* N.Y.: Macmillan, 1956.

Herbs: For food and fragrance

Brownlow, Margaret. *Herbs and the Fragrant Garden.* 2nd edition. N.Y.: McGraw-Hill, 1963.

Garland, Sarah. *The Herb Garden; a Complete Guide to Growing Scented, Culinary and Medicinal Herbs.* N.Y.: Viking, 1984.

Hylton, William H. *The Rodale Herb Book; How to Use, Grow, and Buy Nature's Miracle Plants.* Emmaus, Pa.: Rodale Press, 1974.

* Paterson, Allen. *Herbs in the Garden.* London: J.M. Dent, 1985.

Swanson, Faith H. *Herb Garden Design.* Hanover, N.H.: University Press of New England, 1984.

Trees and Shrubs: To give structure to your garden

Coats, Alice M. *Garden Shrubs and Their Histories.* London: Vista Books, 1963.

Dirr, Michael A. *Manual of Woody Landscape Plants; Their Identification, Ornamental Characteristics, Culture, Propagation and Uses.* 3rd edition. Champaign, Ill.: Stipes Pub. Co., 1983.

Harris, Richard W. *Arboriculture; Care of Trees, Shrubs, and Vines in the Landscape.* Englewood Cliffs, N.J.: Prentice-Hall, 1983.

Hillier, Harold G. *Hillier's Manual of Trees & Shrubs.* 5th edition. N.Y.: Van Nostrand Reinhold, 1983.

Martin, Edward C., Jr. *Landscape Plants in Design; a Photographic Guide.* Westport, Conn.: AVI Pub. Co., 1983.

Meehan, Thomas. *The American Handbook of Ornamental Trees.* Philadelphia: Lippincott, Grambo, and Co., 1853.

Wyman, Donald. *Shrubs and Vines for American Gardens.* N.Y.: Macmillan, 1969.

Wyman, Donald. *Trees for American Gardens.* Revised and enlarged edition. N.Y.: Macmillan, 1965.

Landscaping and Design: To organize, plant, furnish, and finish your garden

Brookes, John. *Room Outside; a Plan for the Garden.* N.Y.: Viking Press, 1969.

Church, Thomas. *Your Private World; a Study of Intimate Gardens.* San Francisco: Chronicle Books, 1969.

Downing, Andrew Jackson. *A Treatise on the Theory and Practice of Landscape Gardening, Adapted to North America.* N.Y.: Wiley & Putnam, 1841.

Favretti, Rudy and Joy Favretti. *For Every House a Garden; a Guide for Reproducing Period Gardens.* Chester, Conn.: The Pequot Press, 1977.

Henderson, Charles. *Henderson's Picturesque Gardens and Ornamental Gardening Illustrated.* N.Y.: Peter Henderson & Co., 1901.

Scott, Frank J. *The Art of Beautifying Suburban Home Grounds of Small Extent.* N.Y.: John B. Alden, 1886. (1870 edition reprinted by the American Life Foundation in Watkins Glen, N.Y., under title: *Victorian Gardens: The Art of Beautifying Suburban Home Grounds, a Victorian Guidebook of 1870.*)

Thomas, Graham Stuart. *Recreating the Period Garden.* Boston: David R. Godine, 1985.

Verey, Rosemary. *Classic Garden Design; How to Adapt and Recreate Garden Features of the Past.* N.Y.: Congdon & Weed, 1984.

Wilkinson, Elizabeth and Marjorie Henderson. *The House of Boughs; a Sourcebook of Garden Designs, Structures, and Suppliers.* N.Y.: Viking, 1985.

* Wirth, Thomas. *The Victory Garden Landscape Guide.* Boston: Little, Brown and Company, 1984.

Flower Arranging: To enjoy the fruits of your labor

Berrall, Julia S. *A History of Flower Arrangement.* Studio Publications, 1953.

Coe, Stella. *Ikebana; a Practical and Philosophical Guide to Japanese Flower Arrangement.* Woodstock, N.Y.: Overlook Press, 1984.

Cook, Hal. *Arranging; the Basics of Contemporary Floral Design.* N.Y.: William Morrow and Co., 1985.

Foster, Maureen. *The Art of Preserved Flower Arrangement.* London: William Collins Sons, 1984.

Jekyll, Gertrude. *Flower Decoration in the House.* Reprint of 1907 edition. Antique Collectors' Club, 1982.

Macqueen, Sheila. *Encyclopaedia of Flower Arranging.* London: Faber and Faber, 1967.

Marcus, Margaret Fairbanks. *Period Flower Arrangement.* N.Y.: M. Barrows & Co., 1952.

Garden History: Fashions and roots of designs of other times in other places

*Berrall, Julia S. *The Garden; an Illustrated History.* N.Y.: Viking, 1966.

Carter, Tom. *The Victorian Garden.* London: Bell & Hyman, 1984.

Gothein, Marie Luise. *A History of Garden Art.* 2 volumes. London: J.M. Dent , 1928.

Hyams, Edward. *A History of Gardens and Gardening.* N.Y.; Praeger Publishers, 1971.

Leighton, Ann. *Early American Gardens "For Meate or Medicine."* Boston: Houghton Mifflin, 1970.

Scourse, Nicolette. *The Victorians and Their Flowers.* London: Croom Helm; Beaverton, Ore.: Timber Press, 1983.

Thacker, Christopher. *The History of Gardens.* Berkeley, Calif.: University of California Press, 1979.

Tice, Patricia M. *Gardening in America, 1830–1910.* Rochester, N.Y.: Strong Museum, 1984.

Turner, Tom. *English Garden Design; History and Styles Since 1650.* Antique Collectors' Club, 1986.

Van Ravenswaay, Charles. *A Nineteenth-Century Garden.* N.Y.: Universe Books, 1977.

Gardens: A look into the gardens of others

Clarke, Ethne and Clay Perry. *English Cottage Gardens.* N.Y.: Viking, 1986.

Coats, Peter. *The House & Garden Book of Beautiful Gardens Round the World.* Boston: Little, Brown and Co., 1985.

Hinde, Thomas. *Stately Gardens of Britain.* N.Y.: W.W. Norton & Co., 1983.

Jacob, Irene and Walter Jacob. *Gardens of North America and Hawaii, a Traveler's Guide; a Handbook to Gardens, Arboreta, and Conservatories in the United States and Canada.* Portland, Ore.: Timber Press, 1985.

Schinz, Marina. *Visions of Paradise.* Photographs by Marina Schinz; Text by Susan Littlefield with Marina Schinz. N.Y.: Stewart, Tabori & Chang, 1985.

Verey, Rosemary and Ellen Samuels. *The American Woman's Garden.* Boston: Little, Brown and Co., 1984.

Multivolume Series on Practical Gardening Topics

American Horticultural Society Illustrated Encyclopedia of Gardening. Mount Vernon, Va.

*Ortho Books on gardening. San Francisco, Calif.

Sunset Books on gardening. Menlo Park, Calif.

Time-Life Encyclopedia of Gardening. Alexandria, Va.

Magazines

American Horticulturist. Alexandria, Va.: American Horticultural Society, 1922–.

Brooklyn Botanic Garden Record / Plants and Gardens Brooklyn: Brooklyn Botanic Garden, 1945–.(each issue is devoted to a particular topic)

Garden. N.Y.: New York Botanical Garden, 1977–.

Garden Design. Washington, D.C.: American Society of Landscape Architects, 1982–.

Horticulture; the Magazine of American Gardening. Boston: Horticultural Partners in association with the Massachusetts Horticultural Society, 1904–.

The Horticulturist and Journal of Rural Art and Rural Taste. N.Y.: 1846–1875.

National Gardening. Burlington, Vt.: National Gardening Association, 1985–.

Vick's Monthly Magazine. Rochester, N.Y.: James Vick, 1878–1900.

Dictionaries and Encyclopedias: For general reference

Bailey, Liberty Hyde. *Hortus Third: A Concise Dictionary of Plants Cultivated in the United States and Canada.* Revised and expanded by the staff of the Liberty Hyde Baily Hortorium. N.Y.: Macmillan, 1976.

Bailey, Liberty Hyde. *Cyclopedia of American Horticulture.* 4 volumes. N.Y.: Macmillan 1900.

Beckett, Kenneth A. *The Concise Encyclopedia of Garden Plants.* London: Orbis Publishing, 1983.

Everett, Thomas H. *The New York Botanical Garden Illustrated Encyclopedia of Horticulture.* 10 volumes. N.Y.: Garland Publishing, 1980–1982.

*Wyman, Donald. *Wyman's Gardening Encyclopedia.* N.Y.: Macmillan, 1971.

Other Smithsonian collections with horticultural materials include:

Botany sublocation of the National Museum of Natural History branch of the Smithsonian Institution Libraries (plant identification and culture)

Cooper-Hewitt Museum branch of the Smithsonian Institution Libraries (European garden history and design, rare books)

National Museum of American History branch of the Smithsonian Institution Libraries (garden furnishings and structures, parks and urban planning)

Special Collections branch of the Smithsonian Institution Libraries (rare books and periodicals)

Warshaw Collection of Business Americana in the National Museum of American History (business ephemera on the seed business, advertisements, catalogs)